Suzuki
Flute School
Volume 3
Flute Part
Revised Edition
by Toshio Takahashi

CONTENTS

1 **Humoresque,** *A. Dvořák* 6

2 **Orphée et Eurydice,** *C. Gluck* 8

3 **Serenade,** *R. Drigo* 9

4 **Scherzino,** *J. Anderson* 10

5 **Serenade,** *Woodall* 12

6 **Serenade a Pierrette,** *J. Szulc, A. Hennebains* 13

7 **Minuet,** *G. Bizet* 15

© 1996, 1971 Dr. Shinichi Suzuki
Sole publisher for the entire world except Japan:
Summy-Birchard Inc.
exclusively distributed by
Warner Bros. Publications
15800 N.W. 48th Avenue, Miami, Florida 33014
All rights reserved   Printed in U.S.A.

ISBN 0-87487-169-7

The Suzuki name, logo and wheel device
are trademarks of Dr. Shinichi Suzuki used
under exclusive license by Summy-Birchard, Inc.

How to play softly (p)

Lip Attack Exercises

Tense your jaw slightly and practice whistling while pro-
nouncing 'Pwhu Pwhu'. Let the air flow between the
membranes of both lips sensitively with a small elliptical
lip opening, keeping medium air pressure behind the
lower lip.

Side View in lip attack リップアタックの状態

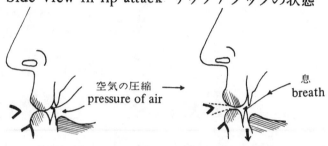

下歯が上歯よりやや前にあることに注意。
Notice the position of the lower teeth.

Main purpose of lip attack is to make a very small elliptical lip opening, and small vibrative membranes. So when
you can get soft and clear tone by lip attack secondly try
to get the same tone by spitting, keeping the same small
elliptical lip opening.

When spitting, use the very tip of the tongue. Let the air
flow between the membranes of both lips softly, clearly
and quietly.

Ｐの練習

リップアタックの練習

フィスリングはくちびるの穴をせばめて吹くだけなので，
小さな穴ができにくい。そこで両くちびるをかるく前にめ
くり出し，粘膜の先の部分で完全に結び，空気を止め，く
ちびるの後で空気を圧縮してからペッと物を吐き出すよう
に，ごく細く息を吹き出し，同時に口笛を小さく鳴らして
みる。そのようにして吹くことをリップアタックと名づけ
ることにする。あごをわずかに緊張させ，両くちびるの先
を小さくゆるめ，下くちびるへのかなり強い空気圧により，
〝プフー〟という発音で両くちびるの粘膜の間で空気を小
さく振動させる。

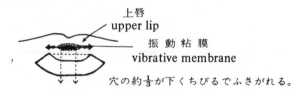

穴の約⅓が下くちびるでふさがれる。
Lower lip will cover about $\frac{1}{3}$ of embouchure hole.

リップアタックの目的は，ごく小さな惰円形の穴を作り，
細く小さく両くちびるの先の粘膜を振動させることにある
ので，雑音のない細い良い音が出るようになったら，つぎ
に同じ小さな穴を厳格に保ったまま舌の先端を使って，ス
ピッティングで練習する。

p＝pwhū プフー
t＝twhū トゥフー

スピッティングの際，舌の先端を使い，細い息によってく
ちびるの先で鮮明に小さく響かす。けっしてくちびるをし
めないように。

Deep and soft color 深い静かな音色で

More air pressure behind the lower lip, but still keep a
small elliptical lip opening.

下くちびるへの空気圧がますます高くなる。
しかしいぜん小さな円い穴を保つこと。

Dynamics Exercise ——<><>—— の練習

To get a louder tone, you should not blow harder. You have only to let air flow between both lips more and more widely, feeling a bigger column of air behind you lower lip. The jaw is slightly tense in piano, but quite slack in forte. The same for the lips, a some what sustained pressure for the *p* but much less so for the *f*. This is a very good way to keep good intonation. The jaw should slack downward.

音の大小を出すには息の強さよりも太さの変化が必要である。*p* のときは細い息を，それからしだいに太い息を下くちびる裏粘膜にぶつけ，両くちびるの間で広く大きく振動させていく。その際，上下の歯の間隔をしだいにあけ，上くちびるをしだいに歯から浮かし，あごをまったく下方にゆるめる。息の方向は *f* になるにしたがって下方になる。深い音色を保つために，つねに腹の底からまた口腔内をできるだけ広くして吹く。

吹口穴の *p* から *f* への変化
Lip opening variation from *p* to *f*

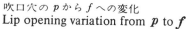

低音 / low   *p* → *f*
中・高音 / middle high   *p* → *f*

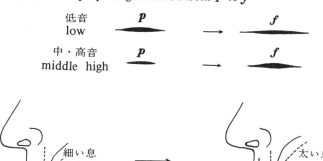

細い息 narrow — 太い息 wide

細く水平な息が出る。上下の歯の間隔がせまい。下の歯の位置は *f* より前にある。
Fine air jet goes forward.
Observe the position of lower teeth.
The distance between both teeth is narrow.

太い息が *p* より下向に出る。あごをおとし上下の歯の間隔を広くする。
Wide air jet goes a little downward.
Observe the position of lower teeth.
The distance between both teeth is wide.

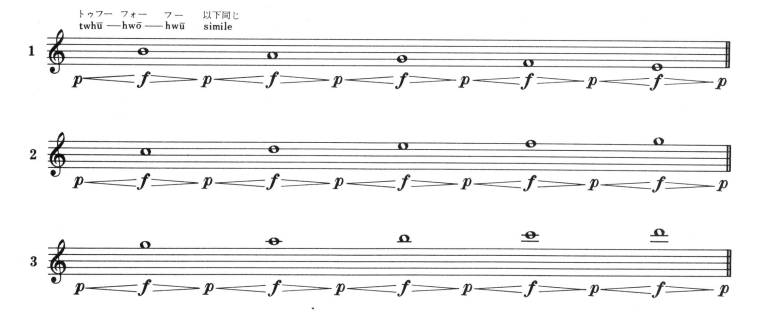

トゥフー フォー フー 以下同じ
twhū —hwō — hwū simile

Vibrato　ビブラート

1. Light vibrato Exercise

String players can vibrate even pizzicato note. This is very effective for a better sonority. Light vibrato means the vibrato played even on a short note, like a staccato note. Light vibrato is the first step in obtaining a fine vibrato. You don't have to practice it with a loud tone. The point is how to give 'life' to a straight dead tone.

1. ライトビブラートの練習

弦楽器はピチカートにもビブラートをかけることができ，しかもそれがはじかれた音を響かすためにたいへん役立っている。このスタカートのように短い音符にもかけられるビブラートをライトビブラートと名付けることにする。すべての楽器においてライトビブラートの習得は，理想的なビブラートを得るための第一歩である。これは大きな音で練習する必要はない。たいせつなのはどのようにして，まっすぐで無表情な音に命を与え，脈づかせ美しく響かせるかにある。

Light vibrato　ライトビブラート

Light vibrato must start immediately with the first attack. Try it with medium loudness. Light vibrato must be always quick and shallow.

このスタカートの各音を粘膜の部分で浅く，速く，鈴が鳴るように "ほろほろ" という感じで響かせる。アタックした瞬間からかけられるようにする。はじめから大きな音ですると失敗するので，中くらいの音をライトビブラートで響かせる気持で行なう。

2. Practice to get a little longer light vibrato

2. ライトビブラートの延長

1.の練習がじょうずにできるようになったら，ライトビブラートを少しずつ長く，2分音符くらいの長さで響かせる練習をする。

3. Practice to get louder sonority with light vibrato

3. 音帯（音の幅）を太くする練習

ライトビブラートが表に出ずに太い音帯に乗って脈動しているように行なう。音帯自体がゆれてはいけない。

Use light vibrato on >　　　>の部分にライトビブラートをつける

4. A good vibrato will occur during a full long tone that began without any vibrato.

The tone color and sonority of a full long tone should be kept exactly the same when vibrato begins to occur. Your consciousness must be kept on the sonority even when vibrato continues. The tone itself must always be deep and full, and vibrato must be shallow and quick.

Good　良い　　　　　Bad　悪い

Vibrato is one of the most important emotional expressions. It must not be created just physically (by diaphragm or throat), but emotionally (by your musical emotion).

Vibrato should not be heard superficially. Firstly time sonority of long tone should be heard clearly, because vibrato is expressive life for tone but never the tone itself.

5. Start to play with vibrato from the beginning

Particularly, practice low register in f and the high register in p with a good vibrato. You must remember that good vibrato depends mainly on suitable, sufficient air pressure working on the diaphragm.

練習　3

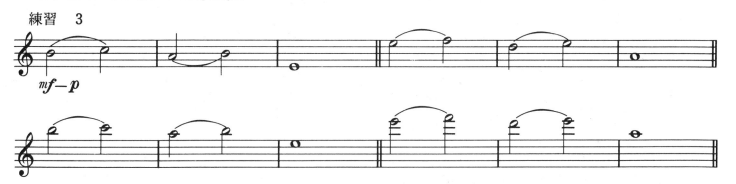

4．太い音帯のロングトーンにビブラートをつける

ビブラートは遅いものからしだいに速く練習すべきものではない。ライトビブラートを完全に習得したものがこのつぎの段階にはいることができる。

まずオーボーのような豊かな音をまっすぐにのばし、その音色、音帯を少しも変えずに息の圧力を高め、ライトビブラートを生じさせて継続する。意識はつねに太くまっすぐな音帯の維持に向けられていること。

ビブラートはハートでつける感情（動）表現の1つで、横隔膜のみを使うと波の大きなうねりになるので絶対避けるように。

太い音帯に乗って玉を転がすようにほろほろと聞こえているべきで、大きな振動のビブラートの中に細い音帯が聞こえているようではいけない。よく聞いてみたらビブラートがかかっていたという響き方である。

ビブラートは音の命であって、本体ではない。

5．音のはじめからいきいきとビブラートをつける

一般に f では低音、p では高音のときビブラートをつけるのがむずかしいので時間をかけて練習すること。

p ではとくに細い音帯の維持がポイントである。p での振動はごく浅くなめらかに、意識はつねに音帯の維持にあるように。

6

1. Humoresque　ユモレスク

A. Dvořák
ドボルジャーク

Poco lento e grazioso ♩=88

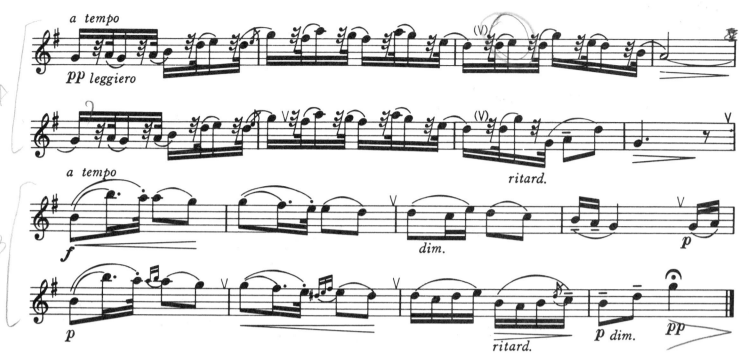

1) Express low grace notes well harmonically.
   Play this part steadily and passionately.

• Try to make a good contrast between the rhythmical
  part and the singing part.

1）低音の装飾音を和音的によく響かすこと。この部分テンポを
　ちょっとおとし，情熱的に。
　軽快な部分と，うたっている部分をよく対比させる。

Special Fingering Exercise

When the C♯ in the 3rd register lies between two Ds or on
the ascending D major or D minor scale, the following
fingering must be used: D of the 3rd register adding the
last two fingers of the right hand. This fingering sharpens
the C♯ a little and gives it a soft quality.

特殊指使いの練習

第3オクターブのC♯が2つのDの間にあったり，ニ長調や
ニ短調の上行音階に現われる時は，特殊な指使いで演奏し
ます。つまり第3オクターブのDの指に右の中指と薬指を
おさえるのです。それによって導音としての少し高めの，
柔らかい音質を出すことができます。

2. Orphee et Eurydice　精霊の踊り

C. Gluck
グルック

Più lento ♪ = 76–82

- Take care of the notes with tenuto (͡)
- The note before the rest should be sustained.
- Carefully express the cresc and stringendo parts.
- Play this piece most expressively and emotionally.

テヌートの音に注意。

休符の前の音を十分長く。

中ほどの **stringendo** と **cresc.** の部分の表現に注意。

思いを込めて，表情ゆたかに。

3. Serenade　セレナーデ

R. Drigo
ドリゴ

- Play grace note lively and expressively.
- Pay attention to the animato.
- Pay attention to expression in part B.
- Play sonorously and romantically.

前打音，装飾音をいきいきと表情ゆたかに。
アニマートの部分に注意。
Bにはいるところの表現に注意。
ろうろうと美しく。

4. Scherzino　スケルツィーノ

J. Andersen
アンデルセン

5. Serenade セレナーデ

A. Woodall
ウッダール

Andante ♩.=54

6. Serenade a Pierrette　道化のセレナーデ

J.Szulc — A.Hennebains
シュルツーエネバン　編曲

7. Minuet メヌエット

from "L'Arlésienne"　「アルルの女」から

Andantino quasi allegretto ♩ = 76

G. Bizet
ビ ゼ ー

- Inhale enough and exhale effectively to play many long phrases.
- Play dotted notes long enough and expressively.
- Profound and beautiful high G.
- Play Trio part rather rhythmically, powerfully, taking care of accent.

フレーズが長いので十分な吸気と効率よい排気が必要。
付点音符を十分長く，表情ゆたかに。
高音Gを美しく，深く。
中間部をややリズミカルに，力強く，アクセントに注意。

16